H&C
AT HOME

For Emily Isles, Lotte Johnson and Hannah Freeman
With thanks to Shirley and Eddie Clarkson, Caroline Ash
and Caroline Jones

First published in 1990 by
PAVILION BOOKS LIMITED
196 Shaftesbury Avenue, London WC2H 8JL

Text copyright © Russell Ash 1990
Illustrations copyright © Joanna Isles 1990
Osborne & Little
fabric and wallpaper designs
used throughout the book
with their kind permission
Henry & Caroline are based on the Henry & Caroline
bears produced by Gabrielle Designs Ltd
and are their registered designs

Designed by Janet James

A CIP catalogue record for this book is
available from the British Library.

ISBN 1 85145 358 X

10 9 8 7 6 5 4 3 2 1

Printed and bound in Belgium
by Henri Proost & Cie, Turnhout

Barbour is the registered Trademark
of J Barbour & Sons Ltd and Pavilion Books Ltd
make no claim to the ownership of it in
respect to any goods whatsoever.

Henry & Caroline

AT HOME

Joanna Isles · Russell Ash

PAVILION

INTRODUCING HENRY AND CAROLINE

Let me introduce Henry and Caroline Bear. *Such* a charming family – and *frightfully* old established, you know. They used to own most of Bearkshire. Now they're down to a few acres and a cottage for the weekends. Here's a twig or two of their family tree, with pawtraits of some of their distinguished forebears (and the occasional black bear).

Major Ursa was in the Indian Army – *terribly* pukka. Great-Aunt Panda was a suffragette which was embarrassing for Uncle Winnie, who was a Member of Parliament when she chained herself to Lloyd George. Cousin 'Crocodile' Koala is the fellow with the corks round his bush hat. A bit of a rough diamond, he 'emigrated' to Australia where he now runs a sheep station that's slightly larger than England. The sinister-looking character lurking behind the trunk is Joey 'Paws' Bear. Every family has its black bear, and Henry and Caroline's is no exception. Despite all his social advantages, after a tricky incident in the 1920s (when he sold Nelson's Column to some visiting American grizzlies), he beetled off to Chicago and became the first green wellington bootlegger.

Then there are H & C themselves. They joke about their initials all the time: when they're rushing to get ready they say things like 'Running H & C in all bathrooms!' Finally there are the little Bears: Toby, Henry's son and bear, Sophie and baby Emily. They even let Ingrid, the *au bear*, join them in the picture – after all, she's almost one of the family.

H&C

THEIR DELIGHTFUL HOME

Henry and Caroline live in a charming London house. It's just 25 minutes to Henry's City Office and five to Sloane Square, the hub of Caroline's world.

It's rare to see all the Bears together like this, relaxing in their sitting room with Muffin the dog and Gorbachev the cat. Usually they are busy dashing around – Caroline attending one of her committees, Henry dining with clients, Toby out at the Bear Cub Scouts, Ingrid at the disco with the other *au bears*.

H&C

Isn't their home divine? It was a complete wreck when they bought it ('For an absolute song my dear – now it's worth a fortune'). It's taken Caroline simply *ages* to get it just right. She decorated it all herself with hardly any help – just a couple of interior designers, an architect, and a dozen builders. The work is almost completed and only Carmen the decorator is left, tackling the final bit of ragging, dragging and flogging. The result is just how Caroline imagined it, a blend of tasteful modern design and comfy traditional furniture; an updated replica, in fact, of her mother's house, and her mother-in-law's and, come to think of it, the homes of everyone she knows.

ACTION STATIONS!

It's breakfast time in the Bear household. Caroline just grabs a cup of coffee; mostly she supervises everyone else. Checking her watch, she ensures that Toby has packed his homework, Sophie has eaten her cereal and Ingrid has every second of the children's day planned.

Caroline hasn't gone out to work since Toby was born. After leaving Bearenden she went to finishing school, then did a succession of jobs; she worked at Sotheby's, as a chalet girl, a ceramic restorer, and did directors' lunches, which is how she met Henry – 'I married the boss!' she proudly tells people.

No one sees much of Henry at breakfast. He usually leaves the house before anyone else is up, or, if he's running late, he hides behind his newspaper before grabbing his briefcase and leaping into his getaway car. What is the getaway from? The organized chaos of the school run! Soon the rest of the family will be under starter's orders and the scene outside the Bears' house will resemble the grid at the start of the Monaco Grand Prix. Range Rovers, Suzuki Jeeps, Peugeots, Mercedes, and Volvos line up, engines purring. Caroline hovvers in the pits, hustling little bears into school uniforms. They wave goodbye – and they're off!

A Day in the Life

9.00 am: Preparations for the day ahead – a powdered nose is essential.

10.00 am: Shopping with mother; choosing fabrics at Osbearn & Little. What *do* they do with all that cloth?

11.00 am: Caroline meets friends for coffee and girltalk.

12.00 noon: To her beartician and furdresser. Maybe a sauna, massage, and paw manicure too.

1.00 pm: Lunch with her sister. 'Just a lettuce leaf for me – well perhaps just a *tiny* piece of that honey gateaux . . .'

2.00 pm: Shopping for a few extra items to supplement the three trolleyloads of food she bought yesterday.

3.00 pm: Caroline drops off a sack of last week's clothes at a charity shop.

4.00 pm: Teatime with yet another friend. What a lot of hungry friends she has!

5.00 pm: Working off some of those calories, she attends her bearobics class. Puff . . . stretch . . puff . . . go for the burn!

6.00 pm: Caroline squeezes in a private view. Pity there's no time to look at the pictures.

7.00 pm: She dashes home to change into the evening version of the outfit she's been wearing all day.

8.00 pm: Out to dinner. 'Dahling! Mwah! Mwah! Haven't seen you for *ages*! How *are* you?'

THE BEAR MARKET

While Caroline hurtles round town, what does Henry do all day? Don't ask – you wouldn't understand. It seems to involve selling debts to Mexicans, or buying debts from Brazilians – something like that. Whatever it is, it calls for a lot of sitting around wearing striped shirts and braces, shouting into telephones and gazing anxiously at flickering computer screens.

Henry works with lots of old school friends who, like him, were raised for the City and banks like Bearclays and Bearings. They have lots of fun throwing screwed up paper at each other and playing hilarious practical jokes just like at school. On one occasion he filled up a colleague's computer with live goldfish. It only knocked out the bank's entire system for three days and cost them a few million. What a giggle! Henry was the first chap in the bank to wear two watches, one of them set to New York time, the other to London. Occasionally he forgets which is which and turns up for an appointment five hours early or five hours late.

Caroline is tremendously supportive and tells everyone, 'Henry's work is frightfully important to the economy, and he works *such* long hours. The poor dear deserves time off to relax.' Sometimes, though, it's hard to tell which is work and which is play. Follow him to the Bear's Arms and spot the differences . . .

BEAR-FACED CHIC

At home Caroline constantly attends to her wardrobe. All those identical crisp cotton shirts with the high collars, those pleated skirts and sensible shoes are *de rigueur*. Like people who drive jeeps in town to show that they are country landowners at heart, Caroline's clothes are a subtle mixture of rural and urban; she wears green wellies and pearls, a quilted Puffa jacket with a blue velvet Alice band. And look at the scarves! Only her mother's generation wears their Hermès silk squares on their heads these days, Caroline's wears them everywhere but – *outside* their coats and casually knotted on to handbags. The quality, the timeless elegance and the style of Caroline's classic outfits cannot be faulted. Even little Sophie is following in Mummy's pawsteps, and so the look goes on, from generation to generation.

Caroline weeds out her old clothes all the time. She gives them to charities such as the distressed Threadbear Bears and other deserving causes; her cleaner, Ursula Huggings, is one of several in the Bears' part of town who scrubs the floors in Joseph originals.

A Loo with a View

Here's one of the Bears' favourite rooms. Like all their friends, they have disguised it as an amusement arcade – and what fun it is! You could spend days in a room like this (Caroline says Henry seems to), reading the humour books – or even the walls; there are school certificates, prizes from Caroline's gymkhanas, cartoons, saucy postcards, family and sporting photos and nursery mottoes such as 'Please remember – don't forget! Never leave the bathroom wet'. It even has some of the things you might find in any well-equipped WC – a good stout brush, prodigious quantities of paper and witty china ornaments.

Henry and Caroline would hate a modern loo – all that coloured plastic, high-tech cisterns and blue flushing water. They were lucky enough to find a rare working Victorian masterpiece, replete with mahogany seat and brass pipework. One tug of the ceramic-handled chain and the water gushes through like Niagara Falls, powerful, efficient and reassuring.

BABY BEARS

Toby and Sophie have a playroom that provides all that any privileged small bear could need. Space invader games bleep, robots whirr and computers blink. Nine-year-old Toby is one of several at his school whose homework is printed by laser. Signed first editions of rare classic childrens' books occupy the shelves. Wicker hampers overflow with dressing-up clothes. Sophie's rocking horse is a family heirloom and her dolls' house is a perfect replica of their own home. Firms of muralists and nursery furniture painters have grown wealthy through commissions from Henry and Caroline and their friends.

There is a veritable zoo of cuddly toys; most of the animal kingdom is represented in one form or another – ducks and frogs, rabbits and foxes, not to mention teddies, koalas, pandas – but their favourites are the dolls of human characters. Sophie and her playmates invent games in which the dolls come to life and they take them to picnics in the woods and pretend to feed them. 'So sweet,' says Caroline. 'They believe they're real – such vivid imaginations!'

'COME AS YOU ARE'

The Bears entertain at least once a week. 'Just having a few friends round, come as you are', they say, but the planning makes a space mission look amateurish.

They discuss the cost of property, private schools, food, wine, interior decorating, their country cottages, the Royal Family and politics. They gossip about their friends and describe their holidays and the latest plays, films and weddings they've been to.

If you were to eavesdrop on them you would hear them say:

'Caroline, this Béarnaise is simply *divine*!'
'I've got this little man – *such* a treasure!'
'*Completely* unspoilt – we were the only English there!'
'Pass the pawt!'

Strangely, they all seem to be facing the same direction; aren't they paying any attention to what is being said? Perhaps they just like the sound of their own growls.

TIRED LITTLE TEDDY BEARS

Unless Henry and Caroline get a decent night's sleep, they wake up like bears with sore heads (some of their less sophisticated cousins are reputed to hibernate for six months at a time, but H & C manage on six hours a night). Caroline's beauty routine takes ages, which gives Henry a chance to read a business book, practise his putting or phone a few colleagues to check what Tokyo's doing (sometimes he can make a billion Yen before his head touches the pillow).

Gorbachev and Muffin can't resist coming in to say goodnight, but Caroline shoos them out before climbing into bed. She paws a page or two of a book – a novel or perhaps the latest faddish diet (the Eucalyptus Leaf Diet was the last one she tried, and before that the Bamboo Diet and H-Plan All-Honey Diet). Eventually it's time for sleep. She dreams of the perfect sylph-like self she will never become and looks forward to another busy, busy day.